Themes for Solo
TV Comedy

Chester Music
part of The Music Sales Group
London/New York/Paris/Sydney/Copenhagen/Berlin/Madrid/Tokyo

Published by
Chester Music
8/9 Frith Street, London W1D 3JB

Exclusive Distributors:
Music Sales Limited
Distribution Centre, Newmarket Road,
Bury St Edmunds, Suffolk IP33 3YB, UK.
Music Sales Pty Limited
120 Rothschild Avenue,
Rosebery, NSW 2018,
Australia.

Order No. CH68783
ISBN 1-84449-619-8
This book © Copyright 2005 Chester Music

Music arrangements and engravings supplied by Camden Music
Cover design by Esterson Associates
Cover photograph courtesy of UKTV
Printed in Great Britain

Your Guarantee of Quality
As publishers, we strive to produce every book to the highest
commercial standards.
The music has been freshly engraved and the book has been carefully
designed to minimise awkward page turns and to make playing from
it a real pleasure.
Particular care has been given to specifying acid-free, neutral-sized
paper made from pulps which have not been elemental chlorine
bleached. This pulp is from farmed sustainable forests and was
produced with special regard for the environment.
Throughout, the printing and binding have been planned to ensure
a sturdy, attractive publication which should give years of enjoyment.
If your copy fails to meet our high standards, please inform us and
we will gladly replace it.

www.musicsales.com

'Allo 'Allo
(Theme)

Music by David Croft & Roy Moore

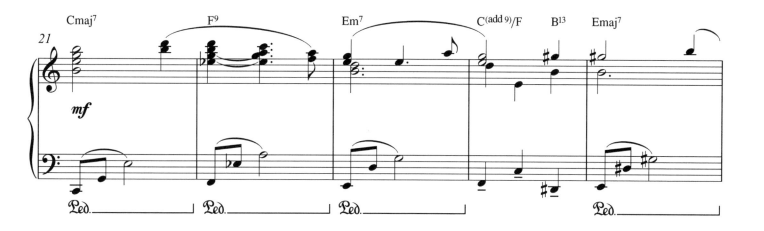

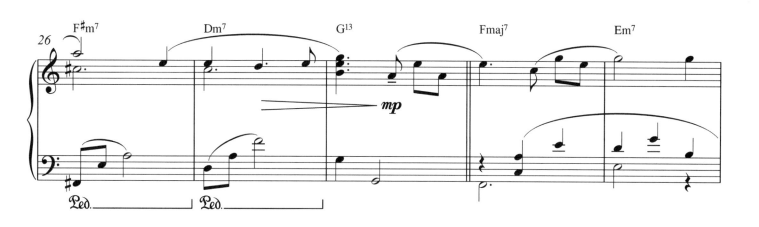

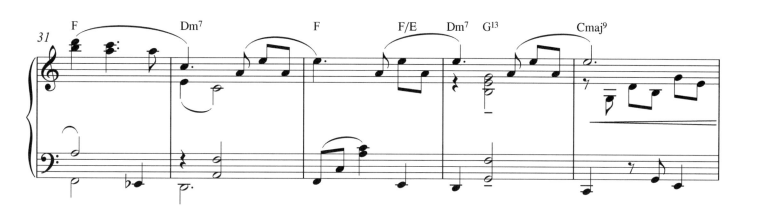

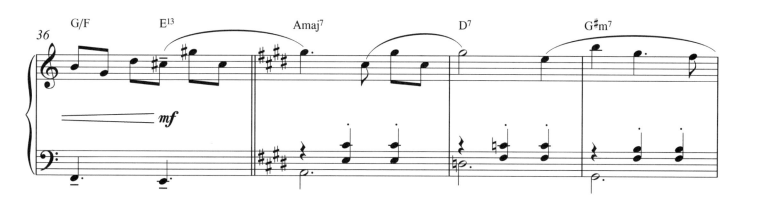

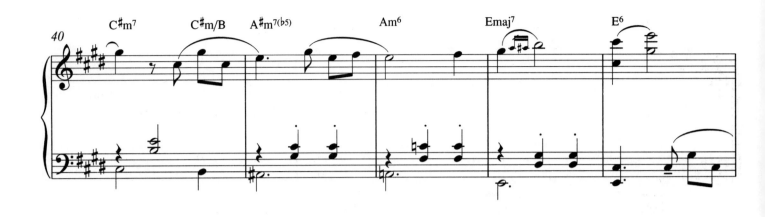

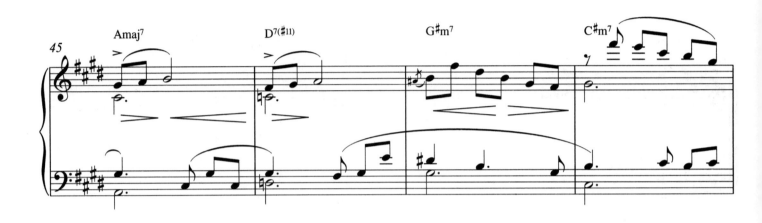

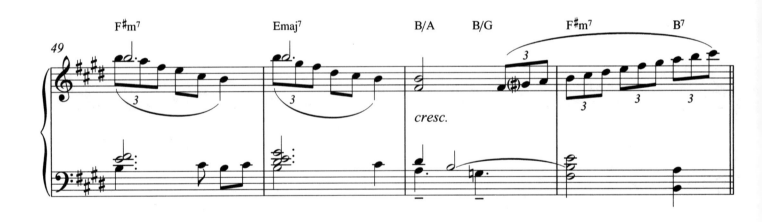

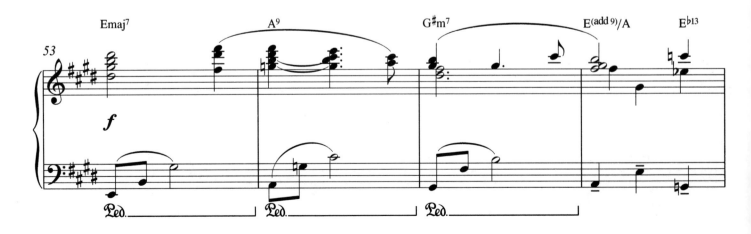

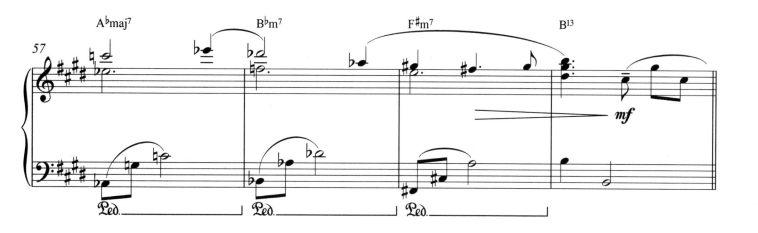

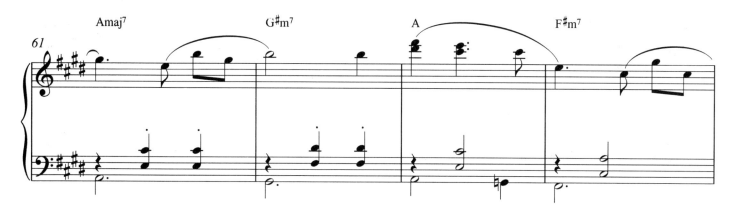

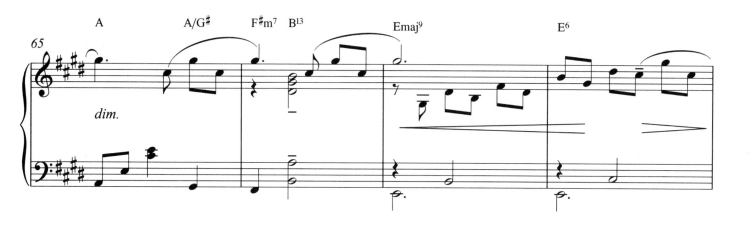

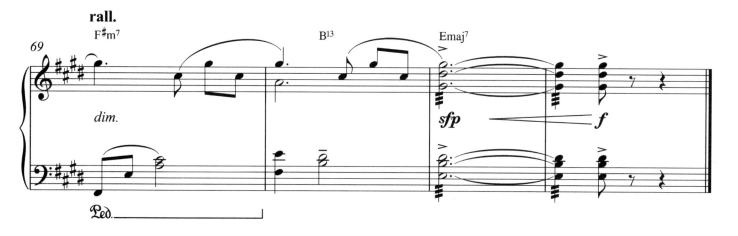

Are You Being Served?

(Theme)

Music by David Croft & Ronnie Hazlehurst

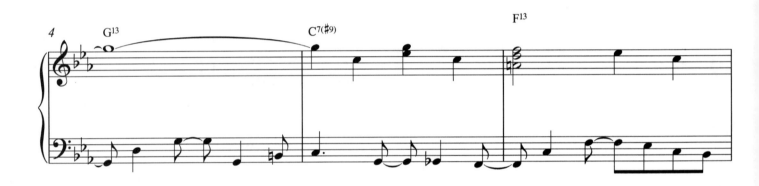

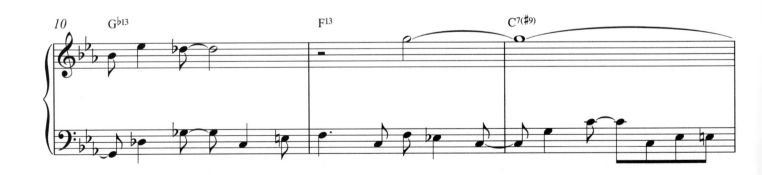

Blackadder
(Theme)

Music by Howard Goodall

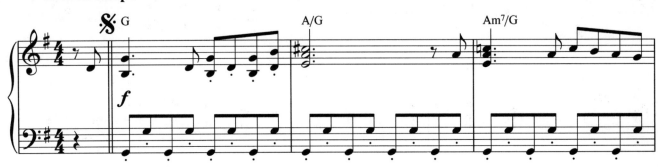

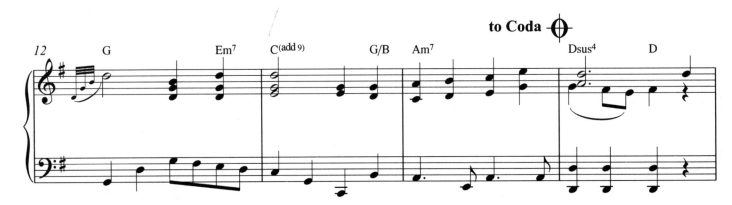

D.S. al Coda

Coda

ff sempre

Where Everybody Knows Your Name

(Theme from "Cheers")

Words by Judy Hunt Angelo & Music by Gary Portnoy

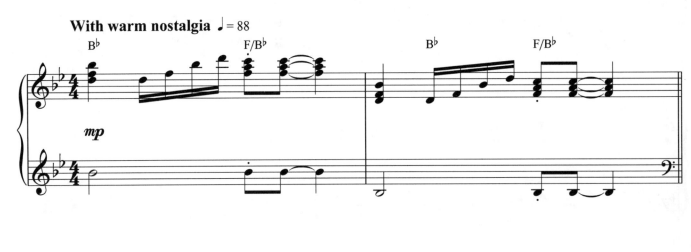

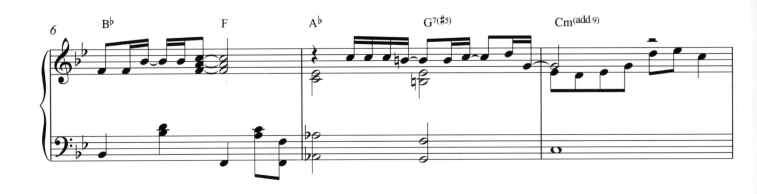

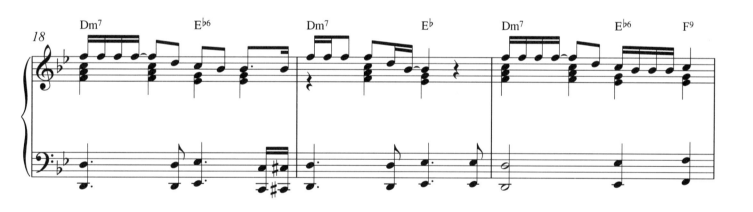

Perhaps, Perhaps, Perhaps (Quizas, Quizas, Quizas)

(Theme from "Coupling")

Words & Music by Osvaldo Farres

D.S. al Coda

Coda

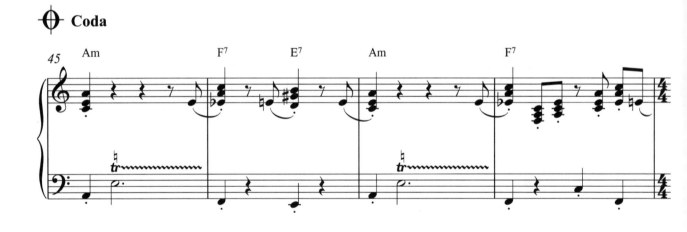

rit.

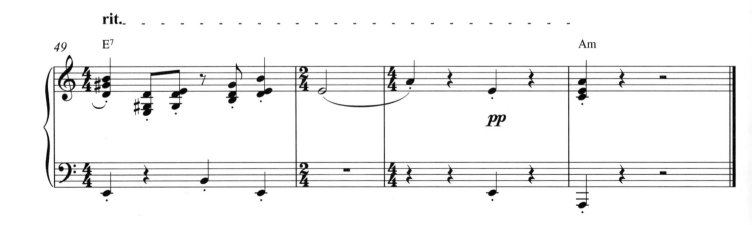

Who Do You Think You Are Kidding Mr. Hitler?

(Theme from "Dad's Army")

Words by Jimmy Perry & Music by Jimmy Perry and Derek Taverner

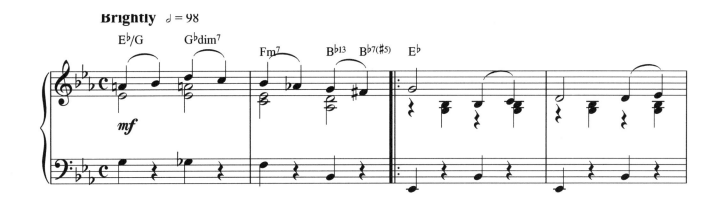

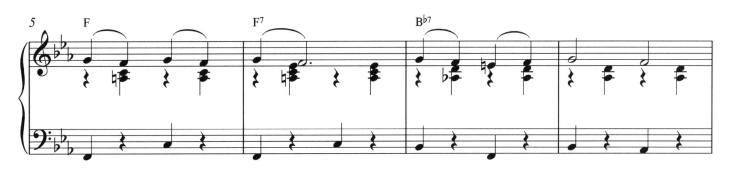

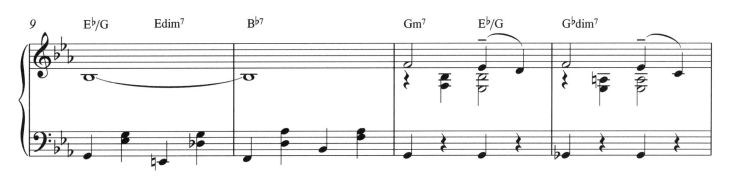

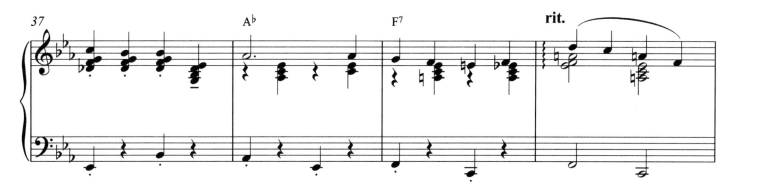

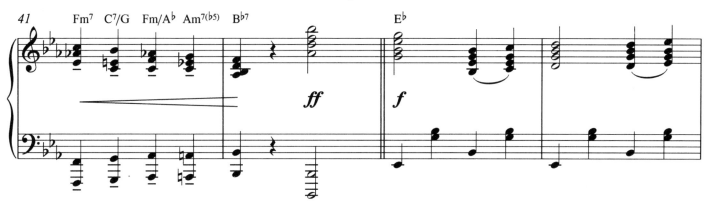

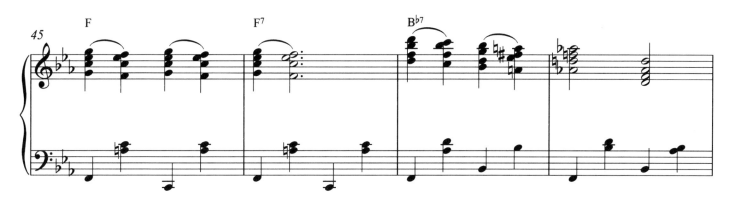

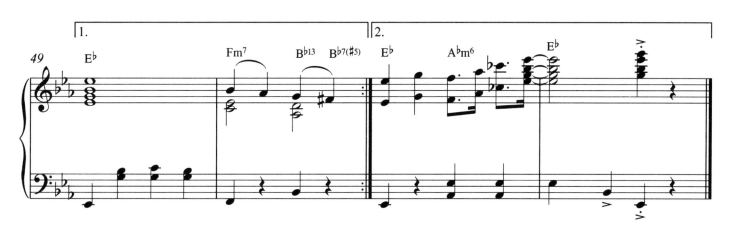

Songs Of Love
(Theme from "Father Ted")

Words & Music by Neil Hannon

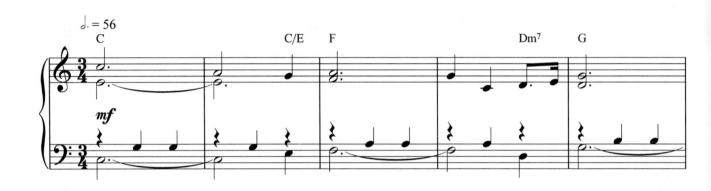

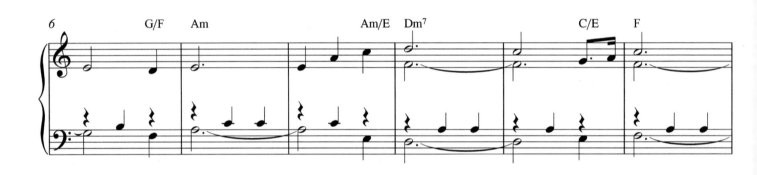

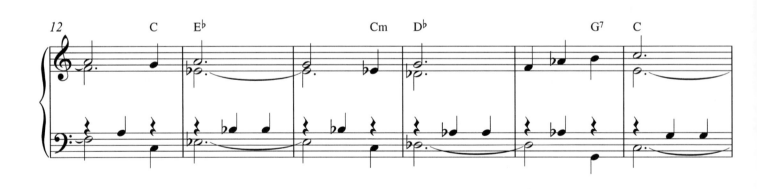

Fawlty Towers
(Theme)

Music by Dennis Wilson

Tossed Salad And Scrambled Eggs
(Theme from "Frasier")

Words & Music by Bruce Miller & Darryl Phinnessee

Gimme! Gimme! Gimme! (A Man After Midnight)

(Theme from "Gimme! Gimme! Gimme!")

Words & Music by Benny Andersson & Bjorn Ulvaeus

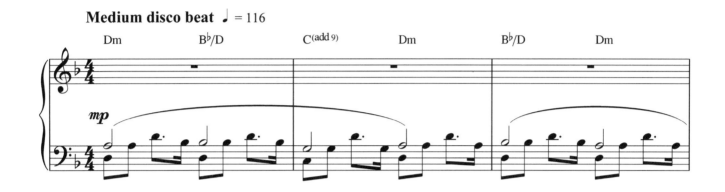

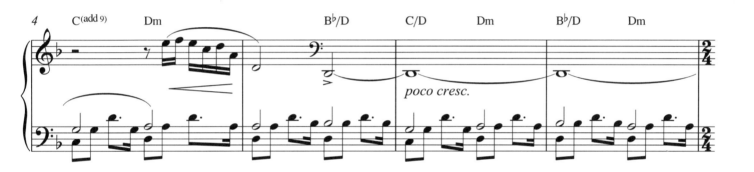

2nd time only

Thank You For Being A Friend

(Theme from "The Golden Girls")

Words & Music by Andrew Gold

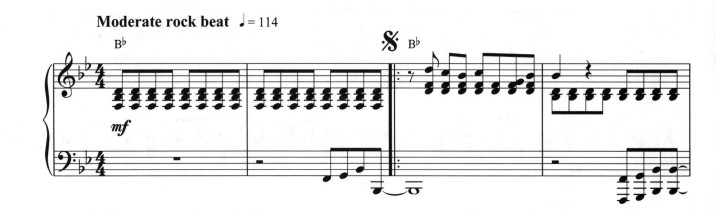

The Good Life
(Theme)

Music by Burt Rhodes

Moderato ♩ = 92

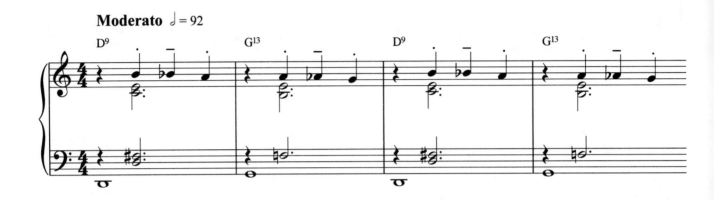

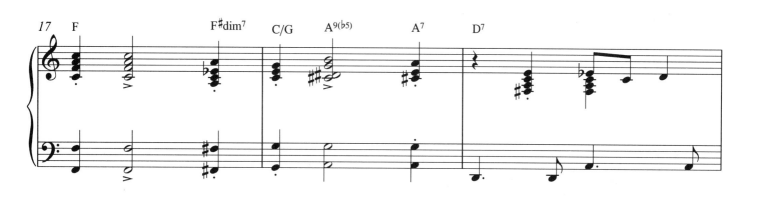

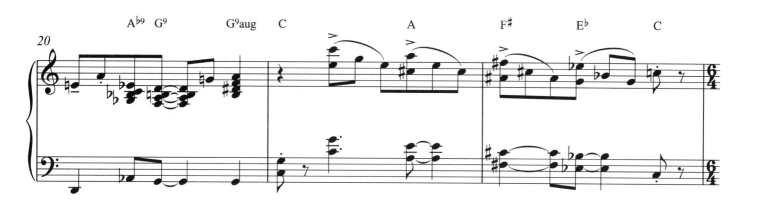

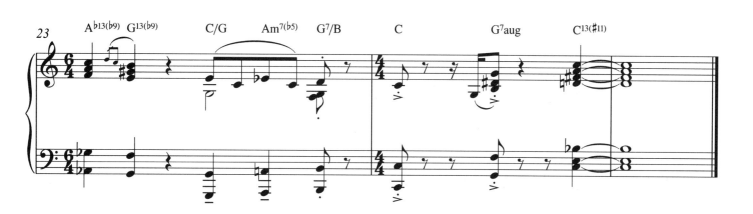

Goodnight Sweetheart

(Theme)

Words & Music by Calvin Carter & James Hudson

Moderato (with rythmic feeling) ♩ = 58

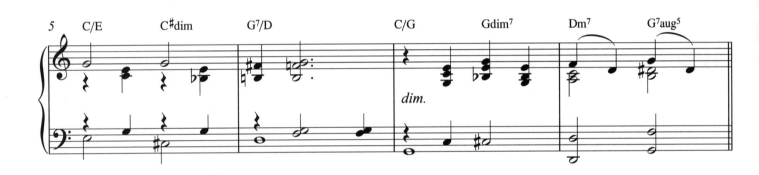

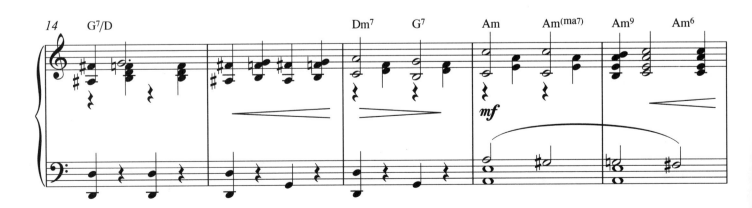

Happy Days
(Theme)

Words by Norman Gimbel & Music by Charles Fox

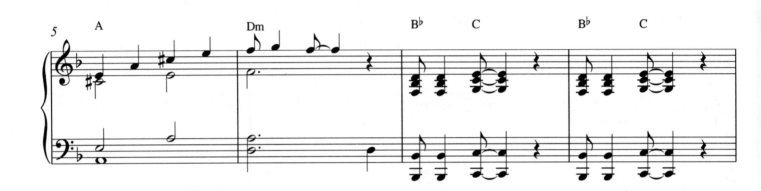

Heartbeat

(Theme)

Words & Music by Bob Montgomery & Norman Petty

With an easy flow ♩ = 142

Hi De Hi (Holiday Rock)
(Theme from "Hi De Hi")

Words & Music by Jimmy Perry

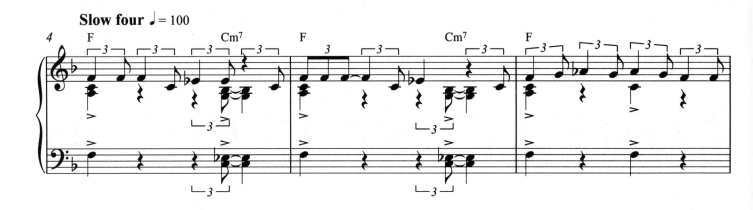

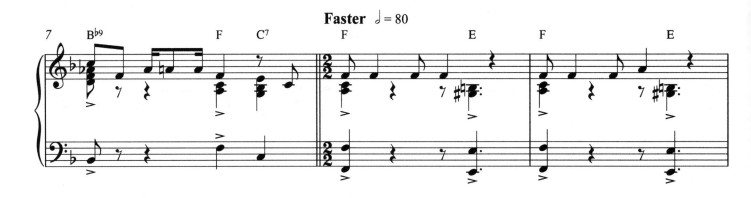

Meet The Gang
(Theme from "It Ain't Half Hot Mum")

Words & Music by Jimmy Perry

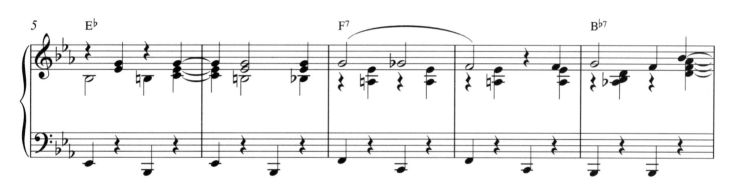

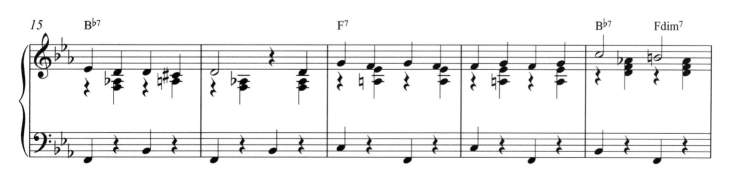

Jeeves And Wooster
(Theme)

Music by Anne Dudley

Steady 2, swing ♩ = 100

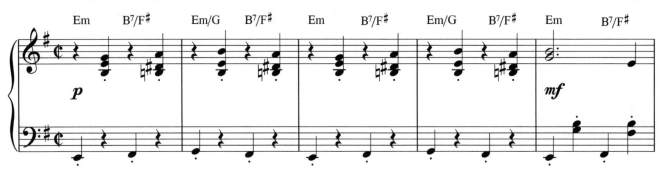

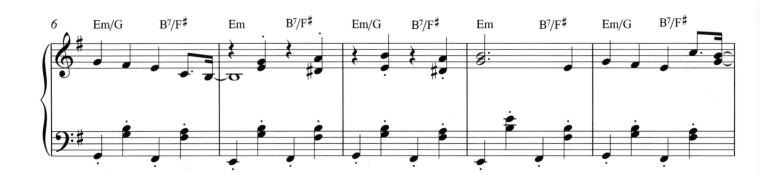

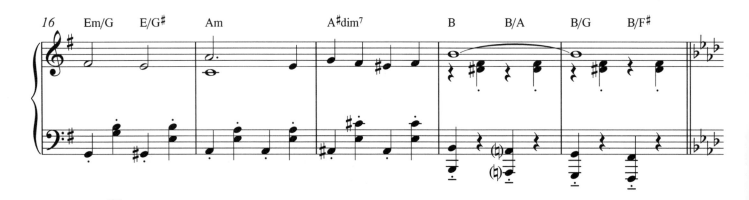

The League Of Gentlemen
(Theme)

Music by Joby Talbot

Rhythmic and sinister ♩ = 96

55

Lovejoy
(Theme)

Music by Denis King

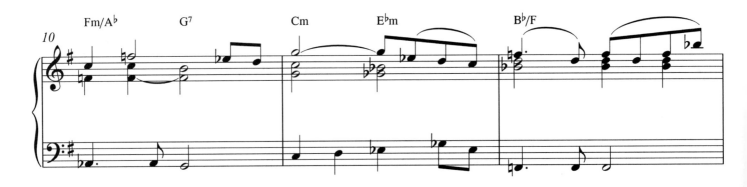

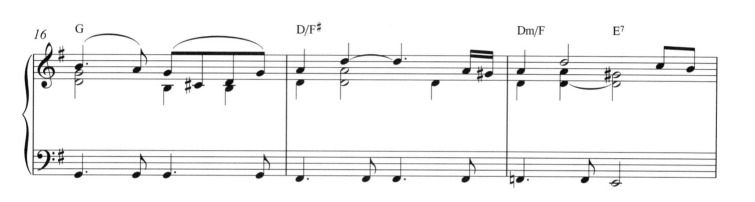

to Coda

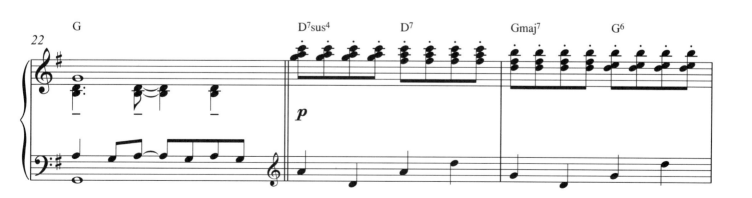

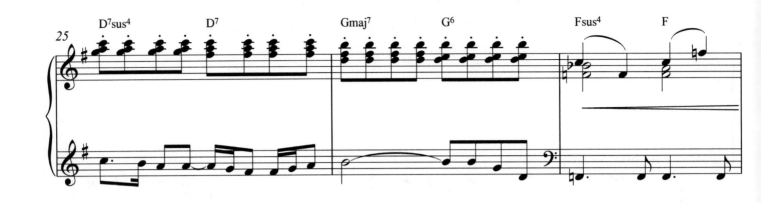

D.S. al Coda

Coda

This Wheel's On Fire

(Theme from "Absolutely Fabulous")

Words by Bob Dylan & Music by Rick Danko

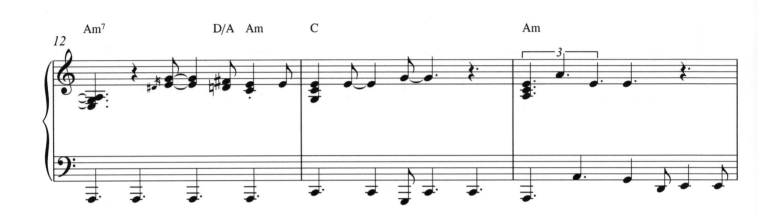

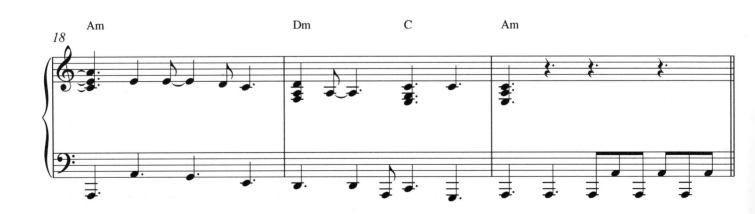

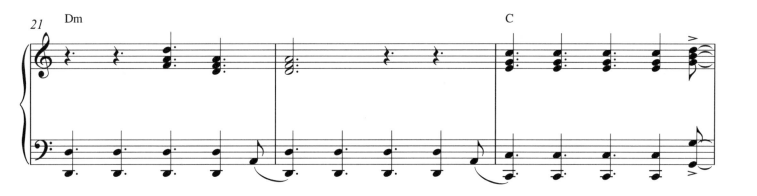

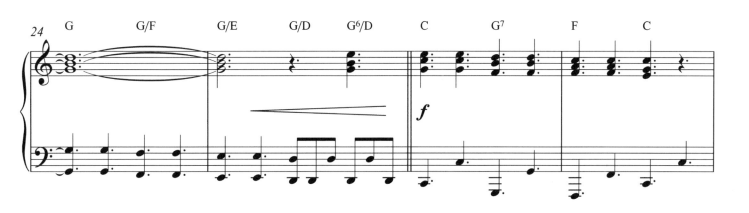

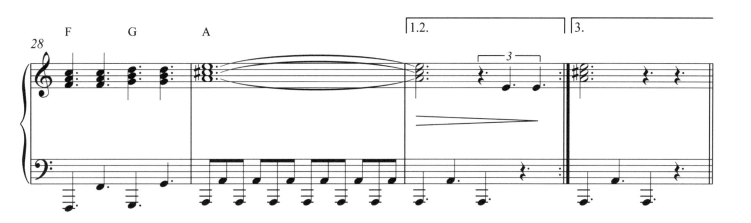

Repeat ad. lib and fade

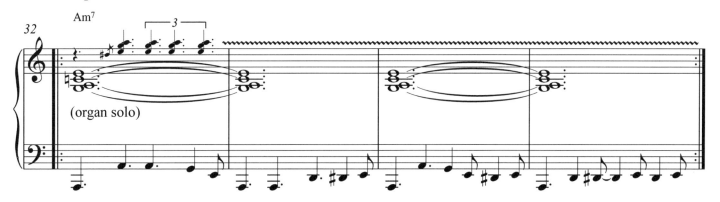

(organ solo)

Moonlighting
(Theme)

Words by Al Jarreau & Music by Lee Holdridge

Mork And Mindy
(Theme)

Music by Perry Botkin Jr.

Bright March Tempo ♩ = 110

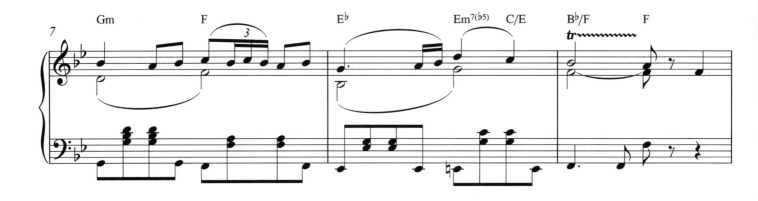

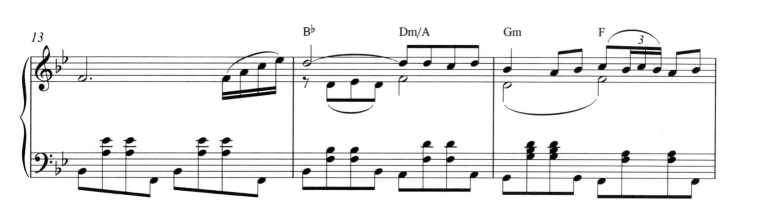

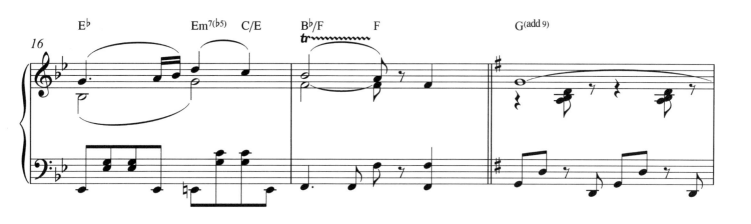

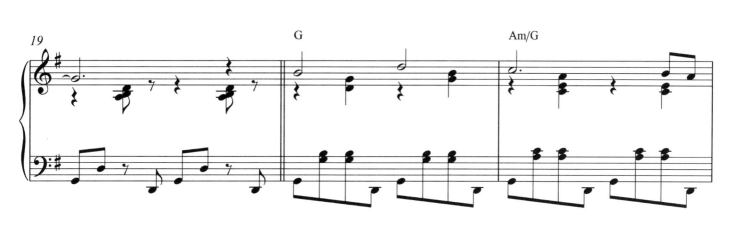

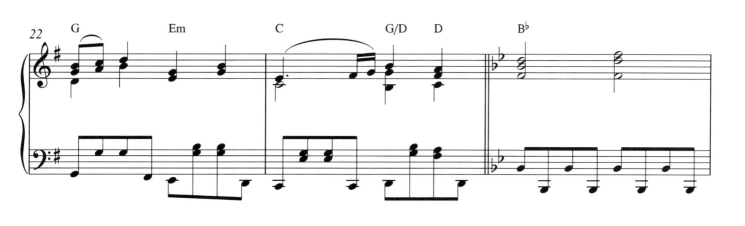

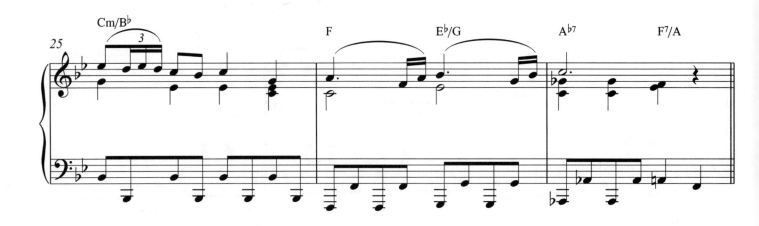

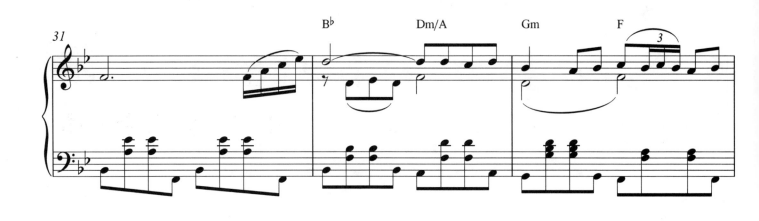

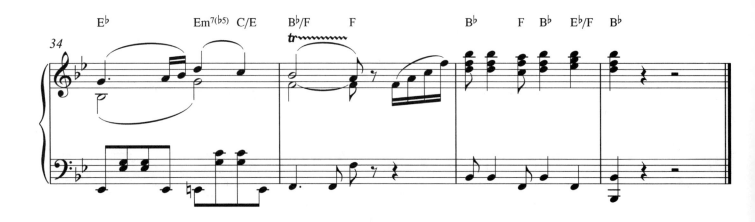

The Muppet Show Theme

Music by Jim Henson & Sam Pottle

The Munsters
(Theme)

Music by Jack Marshall

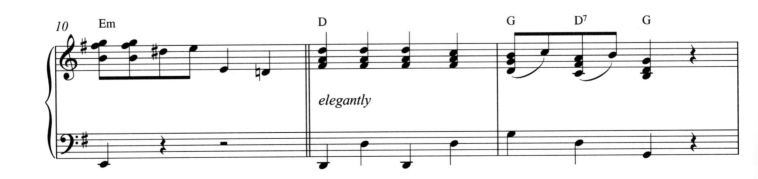

71

One Foot In The Grave

(Theme)

Words & Music by Eric Idle

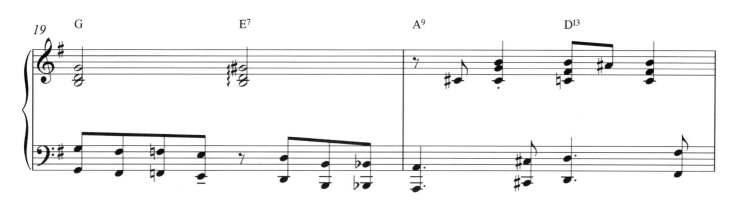

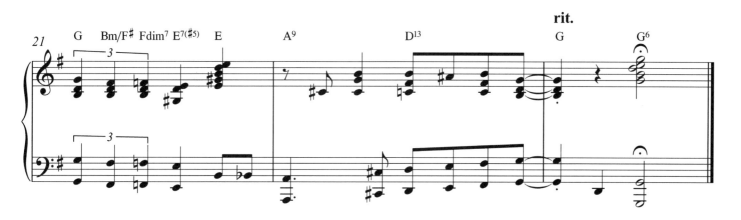

The Odd Couple
(Theme)

Music by Neal Hefti

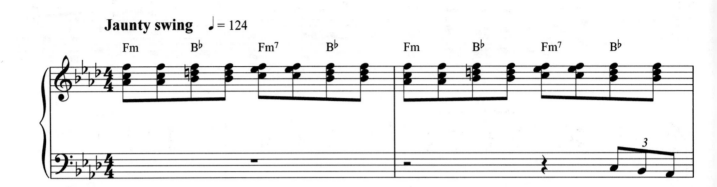

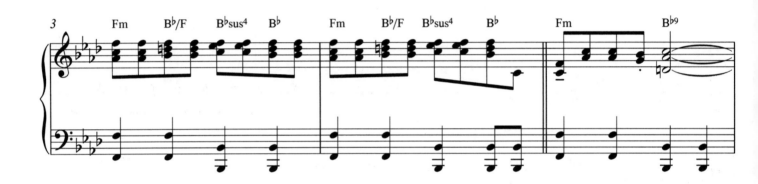

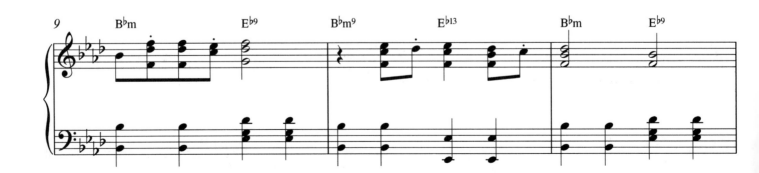

Only Fools And Horses
(Opening Theme)

Music by John R. Sullivan

Only Fools And Horses
(Closing Theme)

Music by John R. Sullivan

Red Dwarf
(Theme)

Music by Howard Goodall

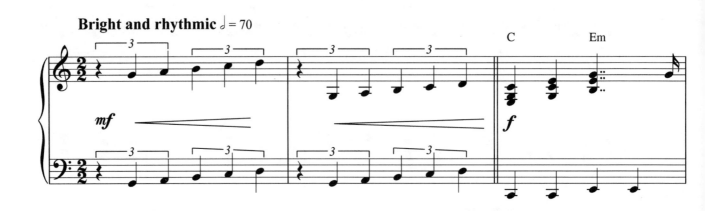

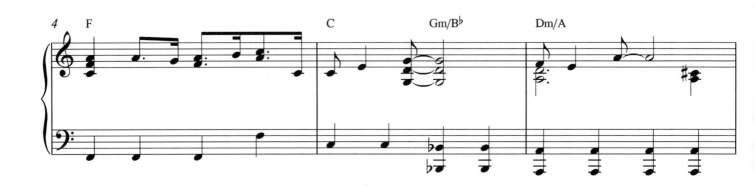

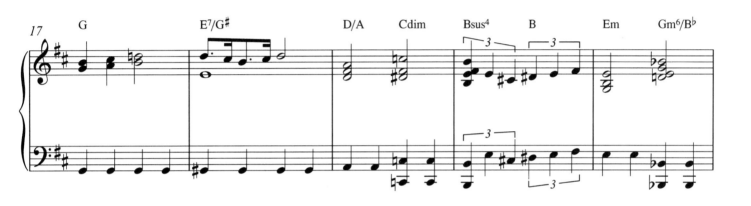

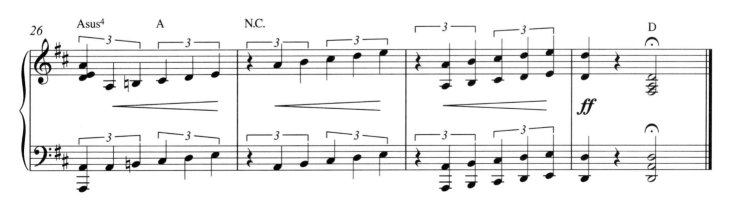

Half The World Away

(Theme from "The Royle Family")

Words & Music by Noel Gallagher

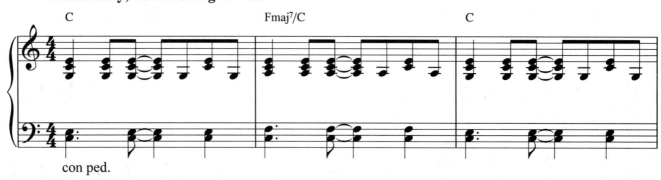

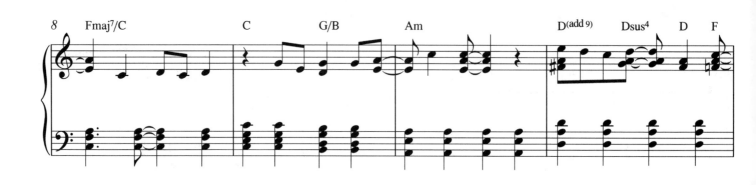

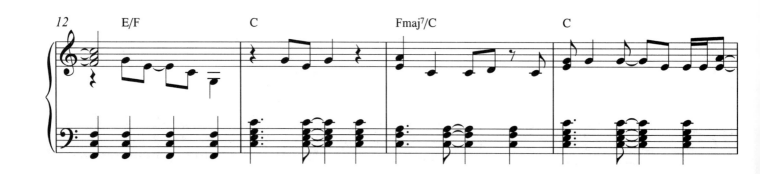

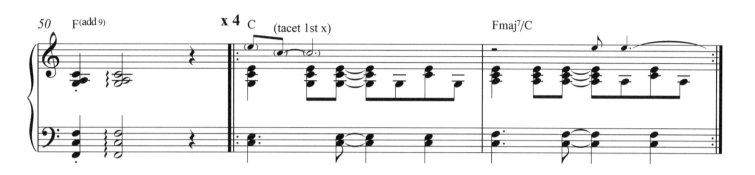

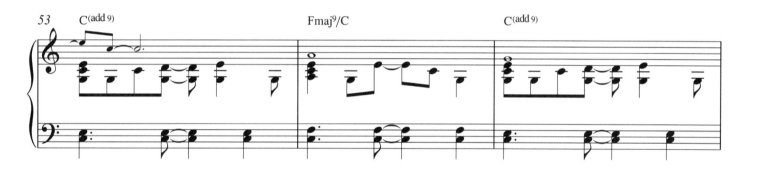

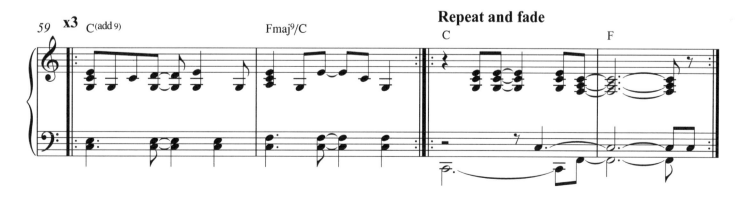

In The Middle Of Nowhere

(Theme from "Smack The Pony")

Music by Buddy Kaye & Bea Verdi

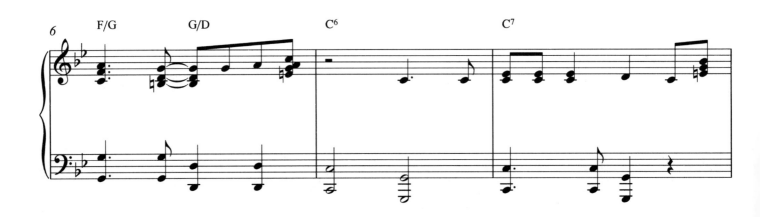

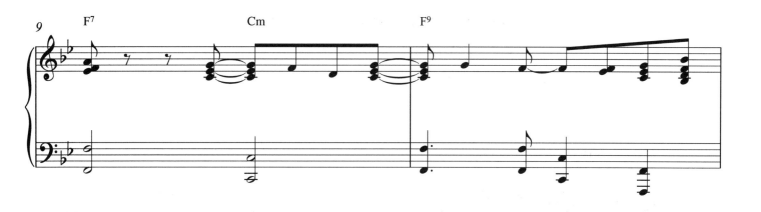

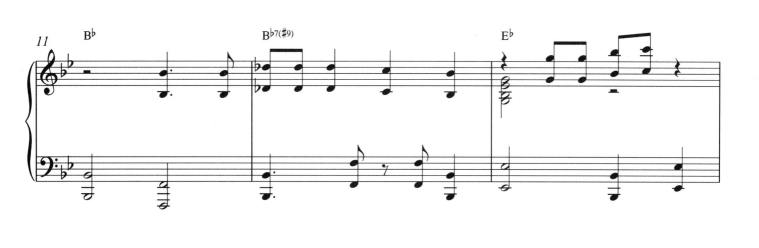

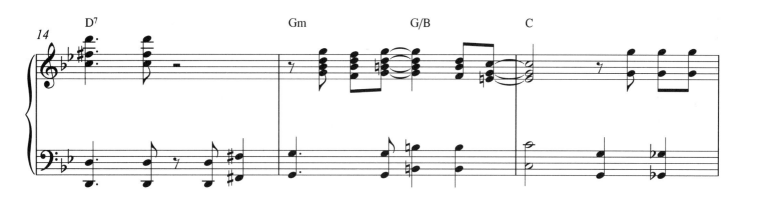

Old Ned

(Theme from "Steptoe And Son")

Music by Ron Grainer

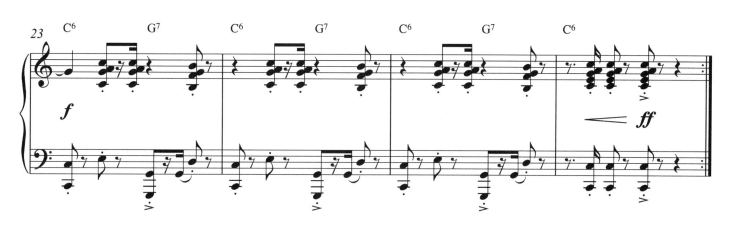

Angela
(Theme from "Taxi")

Music by Bob James

Yes Prime Minister
(Theme)

Music by Ronnie Hazlehurst

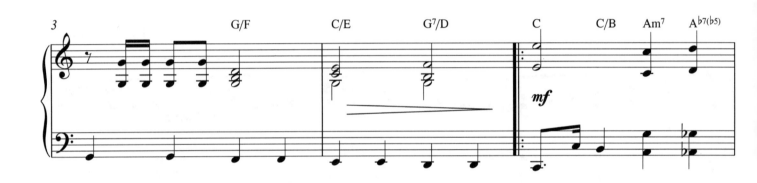

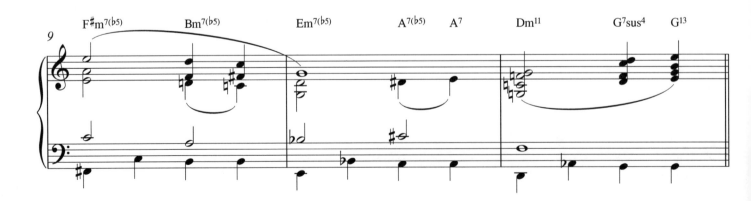

Open All Hours
(Theme)

Music by Max Harris

123456789